For discounts, promotions, and free access to new books in the series, scan the QR code below. Happy reading!

Get my freebies

THE
WOULD YOU
RATHER
CHRISTMAS BOOK
FOR KIDS

301 Santa-Approved Questions To Spark
Laughter and Connection During the Holidays
(Stocking Stuffer Books for Kids Award)

MATTHEW OUTERBRIDGE

INTRODUCTION

The Christmas season is a time of joy and sharing. It is filled with family, friends, stockings, and visions of cutting-edge VR gaming systems that dance through children's heads. But it won't be the expensive gifts you have fond memories of years from now—it will be the conversations and laughter you shared around the Christmas tree.

The Would You Rather Christmas Book for Kids is the perfect gift to kindle hours of amazing discussions and bonding time. It has more than 300 holiday-themed scenarios that are designed to inspire creativity and imagination.

Have you ever wondered if your dad would rather wear green elf tights or wear a Santa beard made out of cotton candy? Or if your sister would rather escape from a snow maze or be wrapped up in gift wrap? Now you can find out! Get ready for some surprising answers. But be warned: some questions might make you squirt eggnog out of your nose!

A festive game of would you rather questions is the perfect way to stay jolly while waiting for the turkey to cook, or the Christmas cookies to bake. You can even play a round while cleaning up the massive mountain of gift wrap in the living room!

Whatever you do this holiday season, don't let the latest digital distractions take away from the most valuable Christmas gift of all: time spent together.

Here are a few ways you can use this book:

- Grab another human—or your dog dressed in a reindeer costume. Go through the questions in order, and take turns giving answers. Whose answer wins?

- Look through the book for the merriest, jolliest, or most challenging questions. Try to stump the person you are asking!

- Ask someone to pick a number. Find the page number in the book, and ask them a question from it. Once they answer, other family members—or talking snowmen—can take their turn.

Some quick recommendations for playing:

- Don't use search engines or any technology to answer. That's against the Christmas spirit! Try putting on your Santa hat and coming up with your own great ideas.

- Always try to answer the question—even if it's hard.

- For extra fun, ask a simple question: "why?" You'll have tons of laughs as your family and friends try to defend their answers.

- The smartest, silliest answer wins!

Are you ready to play? Grab a couple of candy canes for brain fuel, open up this book, and get ready for some festive would you rather fun!

WOULD YOU RATHER QUESTIONS

Would you rather have
Santa's beard
OR
a long carrot nose like a snowman?

Would you rather get into a
snowball fight with Santa's elves
OR
have the Grinch steal your
Christmas tree?

Would you rather have a tiny
Christmas tree like in *Charlie Brown*
OR
a giant Christmas tree
that keeps falling over?

Would you rather have

a big Santa belly

OR

pointy elf ears?

Would you rather have a real

Christmas tree each year

but it smells like wet dog

OR

a fake tree and it's pink?

Would you rather eat an

icicle like a popsicle

OR

eat a handful of snow?

Would you rather listen to Christmas music every day of the year except for Christmas day

OR

never listen to Christmas music again?

Would you rather see one hundred small presents under the tree

OR

five really big ones?

Would you rather go sledding down a huge mountain

OR

go inside an ice castle?

Would you rather have big
candy canes for arms
OR
gingerbread legs?

Would you rather have
Christmas once a month
OR
your birthday once a month?

Would you rather catch Santa
sliding down a chimney
OR
see him flying through
the sky on his sleigh?

Would you rather have
reindeer antlers

OR

a reindeer tail?

Would you rather have your whole
house covered in Christmas lights

OR

your whole room filled
with Christmas lights?

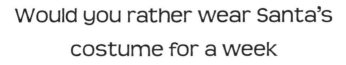

Would you rather wear Santa's
costume for a week

OR

an elf costume for a week?

Would you rather visit

the North Pole

OR

the world's biggest toy factory?

Would you rather put all

the Christmas ornaments

on the tree by yourself

OR

bake all of the Christmas cookies?

Would you rather get ten

gifts on Christmas

OR

wait until New Year's Day

and get twelve gifts?

Would you rather escape

from a snow maze

OR

be wrapped up in gift wrap?

Would you rather sing Christmas

carols at every door on your street

OR

buy a gift for every kid

on your street?

Would you rather give one of your

gifts to someone less fortunate

OR

invite them to Christmas

dinner with your family?

Would you rather build the

world's biggest snowman

OR

get to open the world's

biggest advent calendar?

Would you rather catch candy

snowflakes on your tongue

OR

drink creamy eggnog from the tap?

Would you rather wear a Christmas

wreath around your neck

OR

be covered in holly?

Would you rather have Christmas turkey every day for a year

OR

Christmas cookies for breakfast every day for a year?

Would you rather build a snow fort

OR

go snowboarding?

Would you rather get some coal in your stocking

OR

catch a cold on Christmas day?

Would you rather try one hundred different kinds of Christmas cookies

OR

one hundred different candy cane flavors?

Would you rather open your gifts first every time

OR

last?

Would you rather ride in Santa's sleigh

OR

live in a candy cane house?

Would you rather yell "Ho! Ho! Ho!" every time you walk into a room forever

OR

wear sleigh bells everywhere you go?

Would you rather go to a Christmas tree farm

OR

make a gingerbread house?

Would you rather live inside of a snow globe for a day

OR

inside of a huge hollowed-out Christmas tree?

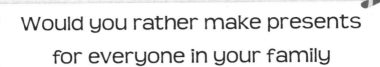

Would you rather make presents
for everyone in your family

OR

make all of the food for
Christmas dinner?

Would you rather have hot
chocolate come out of your nose

OR

tinsel come out of your ears?

Would you rather go ice skating
with your favorite Youtuber

OR

Christmas shopping with
your favorite superhero?

Would you rather know what
gifts you are going to get

OR

be surprised every time?

Would you rather walk around
in snowshoes for a week

OR

wear an itchy Christmas
sweater for a week?

Would you rather unwrap a gift
only to find it's a pinecone

OR

eat a piece of extremely
dry fruitcake?

Would you rather watch *The Grinch*

OR

Home Alone?

Would you rather ride around

in a horse-drawn carriage

OR

be in a Christmas parade?

Would you rather change

your name to St. Nick

OR

Kris Kringle?

Would you rather invent a

new Christmas dance

OR

write a new Christmas song?

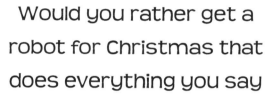

Would you rather get a

robot for Christmas that

does everything you say

OR

a VR headset?

Would you rather have

green fur like the Grinch

OR

brown fur like a reindeer?

Would you rather snap a picture
of a real-life Christmas angel

OR

a real-life elf?

Would you rather drive
a snowmobile

OR

go snowboarding?

Would you rather be a
snowman for a day

OR

a gingerbread man for a day?

Would you rather wear thick Christmas socks during summer vacation

OR

sandals for winter vacation?

Would you rather time-travel to Christmas day one hundred years ago

OR

one hundred years in the future?

Would you rather listen to your favorite Christmas song on repeat

OR

listen to lots of different Christmas songs?

Would you rather wear gift boxes instead of shoes every winter

OR

gift boxes instead of gloves?

Would you rather take a shower in turkey gravy

OR

take a bath in cranberry sauce?

Would you rather spend Christmas in an igloo with close family

OR

at the beach with every person you know?

Would you rather be the director
of The Nutcracker play

OR

an actor in a Christmas movie?

Would you rather have it snow
so much that you can't leave
your house on Christmas

OR

have a green Christmas with no snow?

Would you rather go to your favorite
store on Boxing Day and grab
anything you can carry for free

OR

get $1,000?

Would you rather sneeze every time you smell Christmas food

OR

cry every time you hear Christmas music?

Would you rather sing a Christmas song on the radio

OR

make a Christmas Youtube video?

Would you rather paint your room red and green

OR

paint snowflakes on the walls?

Would you rather share all
your gifts with your friends

OR

get half as many gifts but
keep them to yourself?

Would you rather have a glow-in-
the-dark reindeer in your room

OR

your own Christmas
tree with lights?

Would you rather dress up in
a Christmas-tree costume

OR

a snowman costume?

Would you rather have X-ray vision so you know what presents are under the tree

OR

be able to eat as much Christmas food as you want without feeling sick?

Would you rather have an ice sculpture of a candy cane in your yard

OR

a big inflatable Santa?

Would you rather have everyone love the gifts you give them

OR

know that you will love every gift that you receive?

Would you rather wear winter
clothes that are two sizes too big

OR

one size too small?

Would you rather have teeth
made out of candy cane

OR

strings of popcorn for hair?

Would you rather go to
Disneyland every winter

OR

be in the Winter Olympics once?

Would you rather be able to make
snowmen that never melt

OR

snow forts that never melt?

Would you rather only be able to open
one gift a day starting on Christmas

OR

get half as many gifts but be
able to open them right away?

Would you rather write a letter
to Santa and get a letter back

OR

leave him extra cookies and milk?

Would you rather drink

toasty-warm apple cider

OR

ice-cold eggnog?

Would you rather have toys that

come alive but only at night

OR

make a snowman that talks?

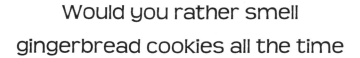

Would you rather smell

gingerbread cookies all the time

OR

Christmas trees?

Would you rather never have
any Christmas desserts again

OR

never eat Christmas dinner again?

Would you rather have a giant
Christmas marshmallow for a bed

OR

a desk made of chocolate fudge?

Would you rather have a
pie-eating contest

OR

a stuffing-eating contest?

Would you rather invent a
new Christmas tradition

OR

get rid of a tradition you don't like?

Would you rather spill hot
chocolate on the couch

OR

drop your Christmas dinner
plate on the floor?

Would you rather play video games
for an entire day during the holidays

OR

find a forgotten gift for you
behind the tree on Boxing Day?

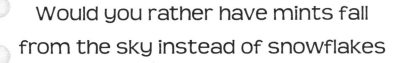

Would you rather have mints fall
from the sky instead of snowflakes

OR

toboggan down a hill made
of powdered sugar?

Would you rather get a dog named
Santa Paws for Christmas

OR

a cat named Rudolph?

Would you rather have $10,000
but you have to spend it
all on Christmas Day

OR

get $10 every day for life?

Would you rather finish a whole
Christmas coloring book

OR

a book of holiday mazes?

Would you rather wear wet
Christmas socks for a whole day

OR

stick your hands in cranberry
sauce for an hour?

Would you rather have
8 reindeer as pets

OR

50 turtle doves?

Would you rather have a red nose
that lights up like Rudolph's

OR

a Christmas light for a belly button?

Would you rather wake up and
have every day be Christmas

OR

have every day be Christmas Eve?

Would you rather wear pajamas
for all of winter vacation

OR

be able to stay up as
late as you want?

Would you rather ride on

the Polar Express

OR

visit a candy factory?

Would you rather wrap

one hundred presents

OR

have all the presents you get come

with ten layers of wrapping?

Would you rather swim in

a pool filled with icicles

OR

jump in a snowbank in your shorts?

Would you rather open a gift
that is covered in glue

OR

covered in pinecones?

Would you rather hide in an empty
gift box and then scare your family

OR

wrap someone else in gift paper?

Would you rather have to answer a
hard math problem to get each gift

OR

have to write a short
essay to get each gift?

Would you rather get a

pet lizard as a gift

OR

a guinea pig?

Would you rather have the

world's longest stocking

OR

eat the world's biggest

Christmas dinner?

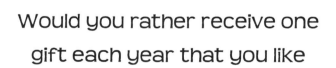

Would you rather receive one

gift each year that you like

OR

fifty gifts that you don't like?

Would you rather give a
bath to seven swans

OR

catch six geese?

Would you rather watch your Christmas
tree fall over and crush a random present

OR

accidentally step on one of
your own presents?

Would you rather get a
handmade stocking

OR

a homemade gift?

Would you rather cut down a Christmas tree with a pocket knife

OR

put all the ornaments on everyone's tree on your street?

Would you rather watch *A Charlie Brown Christmas*

OR

Rudolph the Red-Nosed Reindeer?

Would you rather wear a sweater made of pine branches

OR

candy canes?

Would you rather have your

bedroom floor covered in snow

OR

your walls made of gingerbread?

Would you rather have a wrapped

gift that you can never open

OR

a toy that you can never play with?

Would you rather fall into

a snowbank face first

OR

ski down a small hill

with only one ski?

Would you rather hula
hoop with a wreath

OR

scratch your back for ten
minutes with a big candy cane?

Would you rather put a
big marshmallow on top
of the Christmas tree

OR

a flashing red light?

Would you rather finish a 10,000
piece Christmas puzzle

OR

a 10,000 piece lego set?

Would you rather brush
your teeth with pine needles
from the Christmas tree

OR

use cranberry sauce as toothpaste?

Would you rather imagine any
Christmas food you want and
it appears on your plate

OR

get any one gift that you wish for?

Would you rather make snow
angels in a pile of cinnamon

OR

a pile of mashed potatoes?

Would you rather learn more about the history of Christmas

OR

how different countries celebrate Christmas?

Would you rather sing Christmas carols on live TV

OR

dance in The Nutcracker with your whole family?

Would you rather start a Christmas podcast

OR

a Christmas TikTok channel?

Would you rather be able to
build toys really fast like an elf

OR

be able to fly like a reindeer
but only at night?

Would you rather get $1 every time
someone else plays a Christmas song

OR

$5 every time someone else
plays a Christmas movie?

Would you rather decide
who gets lots of gifts and
who gets lumps of coal

OR

always be on the "nice" list?

Would you rather play every winter sport once

OR

be able to play your favorite winter sport every day?

Would you rather shovel snow with an empty gift box

OR

a tiny fireplace shovel?

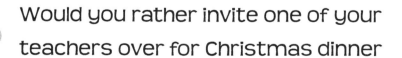

Would you rather invite one of your teachers over for Christmas dinner

OR

make a gift for them?

Would you rather get a
pet penguin as a gift

OR

a pet turkey?

Would you rather be able to
melt snow with your mind

OR

create icicles with your mind?

Would you rather sneak
into Santa's workshop

OR

sneak into a toy store
after it's closed?

Would you rather juggle

snow globes

OR

sharpened candy canes?

Would you rather be tied to the

Christmas tree for a day

OR

wrapped in Christmas

lights for a day?

Would you rather accidentally

break your friend's gift

OR

have them accidentally

break one of yours?

Would you rather open the world's loudest Christmas cracker but get a great prize

OR

open a normal Christmas cracker?

Would you rather get to go to space for Christmas but be alone

OR

spend Christmas around a cozy fire with your family?

Would you rather be the only family who celebrates Halloween on Christmas

OR

who celebrates Christmas on Halloween?

Would you rather go ice skating in a Santa costume and fall down a lot

OR

go ice fishing with your whole family in elf costumes?

Would you rather wear a different pair of Christmas underwear every day for a year

OR

wear the same pair for two weeks straight?

Would you rather do a hip-hop dance with Santa and his elves

OR

try to do yoga with reindeer legs?

Would you rather only eat turkey

OR

ham for one month?

Would you rather lose your two front
teeth during the winter holidays

OR

always have your teeth hurt
when you eat anything?

Would you rather play ice hockey with
a frozen cookie instead of a puck

OR

go curling and use frozen
turkeys instead of stones?

Would you rather wear a winter hat with heavy reindeer antlers

OR

a hat with a small Christmas tree on top?

Would you rather ride a polar bear

OR

a big white wolf?

Would you rather go to New York to see the Times Square Ball drop on New Year's

OR

see fireworks at the Eiffel Tower in France?

Would you rather climb the world's biggest Christmas tree

OR

walk inside the world's biggest snow globe?

Would you rather only have five minutes to eat Christmas dinner

OR

have dinner take five hours?

Would you rather hide the gifts you got for your family

OR

have to find the gifts they got you?

Would you rather have gumdrops come out of your mouth every time you cough

OR

every time you laugh?

Would you rather go to an all-you-can-eat buffet of Christmas chocolates

OR

Christmas cakes?

Would you rather forget to get gifts for your family

OR

find out that they forgot to get you gifts?

Would you rather have Christmas decorations up in the house for six months

OR

not have decorations at all for two years?

Would you rather have a snowball fight inside

OR

a pie-throwing fight outside?

Would you rather blend Christmas dinner up into a smoothie and have a sip

OR

eat a Christmas cookie raw?

Would you rather have a truck unload thousands of gifts for you in front of your house

OR

wake up to a sea of presents in your room?

Would you rather be able to shrink your new toys super small

OR

make them super big?

Would you rather get $200 in gift cards for Christmas

OR

$200 of cash but you have to save half of it?

Would you rather get a
remote control that speeds
up time before Christmas

OR

slows down time after Christmas?

Would you rather get to
work as a toy assembler

OR

a video game tester?

Would you rather eat Christmas
dinner for breakfast

OR

have breakfast food for
Christmas dinner?

Would you rather have a

Christmas scavenger hunt

OR

play a game of Pictionary?

Would you rather only get

underwear in your stocking

OR

only get socks in your stocking?

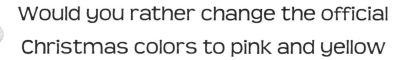

Would you rather change the official

Christmas colors to pink and yellow

OR

blue and brown?

Would you rather have a magic candy cane that shoots lasers

OR

a magic Santa hat that makes you invisible?

Would you rather be Ebenezer Scrooge

OR

the Grinch?

Would you rather be a world-champion figure skater

OR

the world's fastest present opener?

Would you rather bring gifts to people at a homeless shelter

OR

help serve food there?

Would you rather wake up at 5 a.m. and hear twelve drummers drumming

OR

eleven pipers piping?

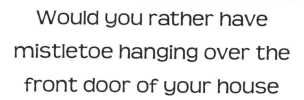

Would you rather have mistletoe hanging over the front door of your house

OR

the kitchen door?

Would you rather get a
drum set for Christmas

OR

a new gaming system?

Would you rather clean up all the
wrapping paper after opening presents

OR

clean all the dishes after
Christmas lunch?

Would you rather train a parrot
to sing Christmas songs

OR

train a dog to howl during
Christmas songs?

Would you rather have super comfy winter slippers

OR

a super cozy blanket?

Would you rather scream every time you open a gift

OR

cry every time you open one?

Would you rather wear your stocking on one foot for the rest of the holidays

OR

wear a Christmas oven mitt on one hand for the holidays?

Would you rather hear the sound of reindeers on the roof on Christmas Eve

OR

Santa's voice coming from
the other room?

Would you rather go to a sugar shack and try maple taffy on ice

OR

have unlimited maple
cookies at home?

Would you rather meet an
actor from your favorite
movie for Christmas

OR

your favorite TV show?

Would you rather get to

drive a snowblower

OR

a snowplow?

Would you rather make a famous

video game during Christmas break

OR

create your own Youtube channel

and get 1 million subscribers?

Would you rather be so excited that

you don't sleep at all on Christmas Eve

OR

sleep so well that you miss

Christmas morning?

Would you rather yawn every time you hear the word "Christmas"

OR

sneeze every time you hear the word "Merry"?

Would you rather have turkey breath

OR

stinky boot feet?

Would you rather have your own personal flying sleigh

OR

an elf assistant who does everything you say?

Would you rather swap all your gifts with someone else in your family before opening them

OR

just swap one gift?

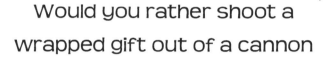

Would you rather shoot a wrapped gift out of a cannon

OR

launch a christmas tree from a catapult?

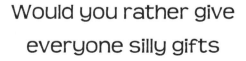

Would you rather give everyone silly gifts

OR

thoughtful gifts?

Would you rather get a
jetpack for Christmas

OR

a drone?

Would you rather dream that
it's Christmas every night

OR

have one free snow-day
pass from school?

Would you rather carry a Santa-sack
instead of a school bag for a year

OR

have rosy red cheeks all
the time for a year?

Would you rather have
Christmas in July

OR

summer break in December?

Would you rather call everyone
at your school and wish
them a merry Christmas

OR

write them all an email?

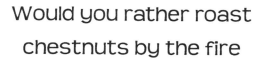

Would you rather roast
chestnuts by the fire

OR

get to taste sugar plums?

Would you rather knock over
a lit Christmas candle

OR

a plate of pudding?

Would you rather open someone
else's present by accident

OR

have someone open one of yours?

Would you rather have an advent calendar
that gives you a different toy for each day

OR

a random amount of money for each day?

Would you rather have a reindeer follow you around for the holidays

OR

a snow owl?

Would you rather have a bicycle made out of an icicle

OR

a sled made out of lead?

Would you rather make a silly face during a family Christmas photo

OR

find out everyone else was making a silly face except you?

Would you rather meet Mrs. Claus

OR

the head elf of Santa's workshop?

Would you rather get lost in a

shopping mall on Christmas Eve

OR

get caught walking in a snowstorm?

Would you rather find a squirrel

eating the food in your stocking

OR

a rabbit in one of your gifts?

Would you rather chop firewood
all day on Christmas Eve

OR

decorate the whole
house by yourself?

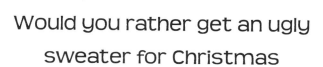

Would you rather get an ugly
sweater for Christmas

OR

a pair of itchy wool socks?

Would you rather open all of
your gifts in ten minutes

OR

ten hours?

Would you rather find a gold
coin in a Christmas cracker

OR

a treasure map?

Would you rather go caroling
with your favorite singer

OR

record a Youtube video with them?

Would you rather only eat
asparagus while everyone
enjoys Christmas dinner

OR

only be able to eat stuffing?

Would you rather change your name to Cindy Lou Who

OR

Holly?

Would you rather walk around in a giant plastic Christmas ornament

OR

be inside of a giant blinking Christmas light?

Would you rather wear a hat made out of wrapping paper

OR

a headband made out of tinsel?

Would you rather make your family laugh so much that they roll on the floor over the holidays

OR

make them smile so much that they cry?

Would you rather eat a bowl of candy with Buddy the Elf

OR

set traps with Kevin McCallister from *Home Alone*?

Would you rather lose power on Christmas day

OR

have an earthquake happen on Christmas day?

Would you rather wear

green elf tights

OR

wear a Santa beard made

out of cotton candy?

Would you rather go for a

drive and see all the Christmas

lights in your neighborhood

OR

fly a drone around your neighborhood?

Would you rather make a

Christmas tree out of cardboard

OR

glass bottles?

Would you rather have a heart that is two sizes too small

OR

a stomach that is two sizes too small?

Would you rather find a doorway to another world in your closet

OR

find a new gift in your closet every time you open it?

Would you rather eat Christmas leftovers for 3 weeks straight

OR

not have any leftovers at all?

Would you rather invent a
new Christmas dessert

OR

a new Christmas breakfast meal?

Would you rather have mild
frostbite on your ears

OR

on your fingers?

Would you rather have a pet
turtle named Ebenezer

OR

a pet snake named Jingle?

Would you rather sleep on the roof on Christmas Eve waiting for Santa

OR

sleep under the Christmas tree?

Would you rather get an Iron Man suit for Christmas

OR

a Batman suit?

Would you rather get one extra gift for every gift you give to someone

OR

get twenty gifts guaranteed?

Would you rather ride on a dogsled

OR

a bobsled?

Would you rather eat too
many Christmas cookies

OR

too much turkey?

Would you rather have
peace in one country

OR

have everyone in the world
get all the gifts they want?

Would you rather get the
same gifts every year

OR

give the same gifts to your
family every year?

Would you rather get
one Christmas wish

OR

every gift on your wishlist?

Would you rather play a game
of bowling with snowballs

OR

a game of hockey with
icicles for sticks?

Would you rather run four miles
after Christmas dinner

OR

wake up at 4 am on Christmas morning
and have to wait to open gifts?

Would you rather hear old
Christmas stories from your family

OR

write your own Christmas story?

Would you rather have
every day be Christmas

OR

have school only one day a week?

Would you rather turn into
a white fox for a day

OR

a seal for a day?

Would you rather know which
gifts your friends got

OR

have one of them share
their gifts with you?

Would you rather be able to pause
moments during Christmas day

OR

rewind them and play them again?

Would you rather spend Christmas in a different country every year with your family

OR

spend every Christmas at home?

Would you rather meet a talking snowman

OR

a talking reindeer?

Would you rather only be able to use candles on the holidays

OR

only be able to use one lightbulb in the whole house?

Would you rather change
the color of Santa's hat

OR

change the color of all the
Christmas lights in the world?

Would you rather have all the
Christmas ornaments grow legs
and walk around the house

OR

have gingerbread cookies that try
to run away before you eat them?

Would you rather have spring
start on December 26th

OR

summer end on December 24th?

Would you rather eat
a snow sandwich

OR

a carrot popsicle?

Would you rather make a snow
sculpture of your favorite artist

OR

your favorite food?

Would you rather only be able
to talk by asking questions
on Christmas day

OR

only be able to talk in rhymes?

Would you rather accidentally break a window with one of your Christmas toys

OR

have your favorite toy break?

Would you rather have your living room filled with sand and have a beach Christmas party

OR

set up your tent next to the tree and have a Christmas camping party?

Would you rather help a poor person on Christmas but no one knows it

OR

have everyone think you helped someone but you didn't?

Would you rather get 1,000
books you like for Christmas

OR

$1,000?

Would you rather swallow
a spoon of cinnamon

OR

eat a bunch of cloves?

Would you rather turn into a 5-year-
old every Christmas for the day

OR

a 50-year-old?

Would you rather get a crystal ball
for Christmas and see the future

OR

a magic carpet?

Would you rather work as
a Christmas tree seller

OR

a Christmas photographer?

Would you rather find out
that all elves are robots

OR

all elves are aliens?

Would you rather collect
Christmas trains

OR

nutcrackers?

Would you rather travel back in
time to see the Nativity scene

OR

see the first Christmas movie?

Would you rather be frozen
in ice and wake up one
hundred years from now

OR

ten thousand years from now?

Would you rather go to church and see an angel

OR

go to the park and see the Ghost of Christmas Past?

Would you rather have your bicycle covered in Christmas lights

OR

your bed covered in Christmas lights?

Would you rather fill a room full of red-and-green plastic balls

OR

have an indoor trampoline during the holidays?

Would you rather invent
a new winter sport

OR

a new type of winter clothing?

Would you rather build an
entire Lego christmas tree

OR

a Lego train set?

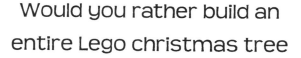

Would you rather change
your name to Orna Ment

OR

Father Christmas?

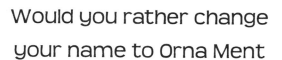

Would you rather use a

huge Christmas stocking

as a sleeping bag

OR

sleep in a large empty gift box?

Would you rather put whipped

cream on every food you

eat during Christmas day

OR

put gravy on every food you eat?

Would you rather have your

whole house smell like pine

needles during the holidays

OR

nutmeg?

Would you rather dress a
dog up as a reindeer

OR

dress a cat up in a
snowman costume?

Would you rather walk across
a skating rink barefoot

OR

wear winter boots on
your hands for a day?

Would you rather be an elf on a shelf

OR

an angel on top of the tree?

Would you rather read every Dr. Seuss book over the holidays

OR

watch every Christmas movie from the 1990s?

Would you rather hear your parents sing Christmas carols out of tune all day

OR

hear the radio play your least favorite carol on repeat all day?

Would you rather get a green-and-red private jet for Christmas

OR

your own house full of toys?

Would you rather drive
a go-kart on ice

OR

go tubing down an ice slide?

Would you rather get a magic
wand for Christmas

OR

a magic lantern with a genie inside?

Would you rather rewrite the words
to Twelve Days of Christmas

OR

Jingle Bells?

Would you rather only be able
to eat food with a toothpick
during the holidays
OR
with a straw?

Would you rather have the
president over for Christmas dinner
OR
your favorite superhero?

Would you rather accidentally
break an ornament
OR
a Christmas mug?

Would you rather only be able to use your teeth to open gifts

OR

your feet?

Would you rather have lots of Christmas cookie crumbs in your hair for the whole day

OR

brussels sprouts in your pockets?

Would you rather have the North Pole be in one of the rooms in your house

OR

have a toy shop room?

Would you rather forget Christmas
day as soon as it's over
OR
shave your head every Boxing Day?

Would you rather have
candy cane earrings
OR
gumdrop fingertips?

Would you rather find a smelly
sock in your stocking
OR
a moldy banana?

Would you rather have no
more turkeys in the world
OR
no more potatoes?

Would you rather have a snowball fight
but get hit in the face every five minutes
OR
go skiing but fall down
every five minutes?

Would you rather have
Santa's voice all the time
OR
a high-pitched elf voice?

Would you rather have a

hockey rink in your house

OR

a half-pipe for snowboarding?

Would you rather your whole

family chew Christmas dinner

with their mouths open

OR

drink really loudly?

Would you rather dye your hair

red and green for one year

OR

only wear red and green

clothes for one year?

Would you rather try Christmas
food from every country
OR
get a small Christmas gift
from every country?

Would you rather have
a pet polar bear
OR
a pet walrus?

Would you rather be able to teleport
to other houses on Christmas day
OR
have a VR headset that
shows you how other families
celebrate Christmas?

Would you rather drink ten cups
of hot cocoa with marshmallows
OR
have ten plates of
Christmas log cake?

Would you rather sled
down Mt. Everest
OR
fly to the North Pole on a fighter jet?

Would you rather get your
head stuck in a turkey
OR
your hand stuck in a jar of gravy?

Would you rather brush your teeth with custard sauce

OR

wash your face with eggnog?

Would you rather get one Christmas gift for every nice thing you do for someone in the year

OR

get $1 for every nice thing you say to someone?

Would you rather wear a snowsuit inside for a day

OR

shorts and a t-shirt outside for a day in winter?

Would you rather read Santa's naughty

OR

nice list

OR

write a new naughty

OR

nice list and swap it with the original?

Would you rather walk

barefoot on hot chestnuts

OR

across a pool of chutney?

Would you rather carry a

Christmas tree for one mile

OR

pull a sleigh filled with

presents for one mile?

Would you rather have icicles

come out of your nose

when you go outside

OR

a beard of frost grow on your face?

Made in the USA
Columbia, SC
09 December 2022

73337135R00061